Ros Ba

Noisy

ACKNOWLEDGEMENTS

Written by: Ros Bayley
(in association with Lynn Broadbent)

Illustrated by: Peter Scott

Produced by: Lynda Lawrence.

Published by: Lawrence Educational
Unit 21, Brookvale Trading Estate,
Birmingham B6 7AQ

©   Lawrence Educational 2005.

ISBN: 1-903670-44-6

CONTENTS

Introduction

We all need a sense of steady beat when performing any task involving sophisticated movement, i.e. when walking, dancing, writing, cutting with scissors, hammering in a nail or drawing. In fact, it is so essential that if someone lacks beat awareness, he or she usually have difficulty with both gross and fine motor skills.

Recent studies have even shown a correlation of beat competency to school achievement that exceeds that of either social class or mother's education, these latter two being the usual predictors of school success. By helping children to develop beat competency we can improve their chances of success.

There are a wide range of ways in which we can help children to develop beat competency, but the more that young children have opportunities to engage in singing, dancing and rapping and playing with instruments, jingles and rhymes, the better they will get.

The rhymes in this book can all be chanted to a steady beat, or if you prefer, you can make up simple tunes to go with them. The important thing is simply to enjoy chanting them and to loose yourself in the musicality of language!

Ros Bayley

My Noisy Phone

I've got a phone that goes
DING A LING LING
DING A LING LING
Every time it rings

I've got a phone that goes
BEEP BEEP BEEP
BEEP BEEP BEEP
Even when I sleep

I've got a phone that goes
SHE-BOP SHE-BOP SHE-BOP
SHE-BOP SHE-BOP SHE-BOP
When I'm standing in the shop

I've got a phone that goes
PING PING PING
PING PING PING
It's such a noisy thing!

Encourage the children to think of other ring tones for the phone.

Down on the Farm

Down on the farm in the middle of the night

I heard a noise that gave me such a fright

So I got out of bed to see what I could see

And there behind the old oak tree…

The cows went moo

The sheep went baa

The pigs went oink

The hens went cluck

The ducks went quack

The turkeys went gobble

And the dogs went woof as loudly

as they could!

I Can Hear the Rain

Pitter-patter pitter-patter

I can hear the rain

Pitter-patter pitter-patter

On my window pane

Splish-splosh splish-splosh

Going down the drain

Pitter-patter pitter-patter

Here it comes again.

The Fire Engine

Can you hear the fire engine?

Nee-nor nee-nor

Can you hear the fire engine?

Racing down the street?

Can you see the fire fighters?

Nee-nor nee-nor

Can you see the fire fighters?

Shah and Kate and Pete.

The Train

Clickety-clack clickety-clack

Went the train as it rolled down the track

Clickety-clack clickety-clack

All the way there and all the way back.

It stopped at the station

The people got out

We're off again now!

We heard the guard shout.

Once they know the rhyme the children might like to try walking in line as they recite the rhyme.

The Door Bell

The bell on our door

Rings all day long

It rings and rings

And this is it's song…..

DING DONG DING DONG
DING DONG DING DONG

It sings all day

And it never goes wrong.

Once the children are familiar with the rhyme they
may like to think of different 'rings' for the bell.

It's a Goal!

Racing down the football pitch

Heading for the net

Must win all the tackles

'Cause we haven't scored yet.

Come on number _ *(insert number)*

And please don't hit the pole

Yes yes yes yes

Yes IT'S A GOAL!

In the Bath

I was lying in the bath

When my mum pulled out the plug

Out went the water

Glug glug glug.

It went gurgle gurgle gurgle

As it went down the drain

Out went my mum

So I filled it up again.

My Little Sister

My little sister

Sings all day long

She never shuts up

And I think it's wrong

La la la la

Trips off her tongue

And we all wish

That she'd learn a new song.

Once the children are familiar with the rhyme they can substitute the la la la la for a different sound.

Noises in the Night

One dark night from all around

I heard the most amazing sounds

The clock went tick

The tap went drip

The owl went hoot

My sister played upon the flute

I heard a door go bang

A dustbin lid go clang

I heard my dad go SNORE

I said I CANNOT STAND THIS ANYMORE.

The children may like to add further noises that can be heard at night.

The Noisy Birds

Early in the morning as the sun comes up

Out come the birds to strut their stuff.

Tweet tweet tweet

Tweet tweet tweet

Tweet tweet tweet

And I can't sleep.

Caw caw caw

Caw caw caw

Caw caw caw

Please don't do it anymore.

Cock-a-doodle-do

Cock-a-doodle-do

Cock-a-doodle-do

Oh shut up DO!

On the Dodgems

Bim bam zoom bang

In the dodgem car

Me and mum and Uncle John

We scream and hold the bar.

Someone's going to hit us

They're coming up behind

OH NO! screamed mum

WATCH OUT! said John

Then in a flash

OH WHAT A CRASH!

My Brother's Drum

My brother's got a drum

And I said to my mum

PLEASE DON'T LET HIM PLAY
IT ALL DAY LONG.

Bang-tiddley bang tiddley

BOOM BOOM BOOM!

What an awful noise

Coming from his room.

*The children can generate ideas for other noises
made by the drum*

Flying Through Space

In our spaceship

We fly through space

Off we race

To a very special place.

Five, four, three, two, one,
BLAST OFF!

In our spaceship

We fly through space

Off we race

Back to base.

Five, four, three, two, one
BLAST OFF!

On the Beach

I stood on the beach

I looked out to sea

In came the waves

Heading straight for ME

The thunder rolled (children
make sound of thunder)

The lightning flashed

I turned around

And off I dashed!

This is My Beat

I was walking down the street

Dragging my feet

Looking for a beat

This is my beat.....

One child claps a beat for the others to copy. The
rhyme is then repeated and the next child has a go.

We hope you have enjoyed our 'Noisy Raps'.

Other books in the same series are:

Ros Bayley's **Animal Raps**   ISBN: 1-903670-38-1

Ros Bayley's **Action Raps**   ISBN: 1-903670-42-X

Ros Bayley's **Beanbag Raps**   ISBN: 1-903670-44-6

Additional rhymes and further guidance on developing children's beat competency can be found in our '**Helping Young Children With Steady Beat**' resource pack.

Included with this pack is a small cuddly toy called BEAT BABY, who can be used at the beginning and end of sessions to help focus the children and to bring emotional engagement to the whole process.

ISBN: 1-903670-26-4

For further details of these and our many other publications, visit our website:

www.educationalpublications.com